Prom Praise

Solos
Volume Two

Artistic Director:
Noël Tredinnick

Editor:
Timothy Robb

CHRISTIAN FOCUS

Langham Arts

Christian Focus Publications
Geanies House, Fearn, Tain, Ross-shire, Scotland , IV20 1TW

First published in 1997 by Christian Focus Publications Ltd.

British Library Cataloguing in Publication Data
Prom Praise Solos : Volume Two
   1. Songs, Christian
   I. Robb, Timothy

ISBN 1-85792-384-7

Cover Design by Impression Litho, Slough

Printed in Great Britain by J W Arrowsmith Ltd, Bristol.

Prom Praise Solos
Volume Two

Artistic Director: Noël Tredinnick
Editor: Timothy Robb

Recordings

Some of the songs in this collection have been recorded and are available on the following albums:

As Water To The Thirsty	Crown Him - Prom Praise At Wembley	Cassette	WSTC	9693
	Hymns For Today's Church	Cassette	LANGC	002
	Tell Out My Soul	Cassette	KMC	936
		CD	KMCD	936
Eagles Fly	When All's Said And Done	Cassette	MEK	001
He Became Like A Man (The Name Of Jesus)	Get On Board!	Cassette	FISHC	1
		CD	FISHD	1
He's Alive (A Song For Easter)	Prom Praise Festival	Cassette	LANGC	010
		CD	LANGD	010
Thorns In The Straw	Kendrick Collection Live!	Cassette	LANGC	011
		CD	LANGD	011
With Loving Hands	Hymns For Today's Church	Cassette	LANGC	002
	Prom Praise Festival	Cassette	LANGC	010
		CD	LANGD	010
Words Of Praise	Prom Praise On Tour	Cassette	LANGC	009
		CD	LANGD	009

Recordings and orchestral parts are available from:
Langham Arts, St Paul's Church, Robert Adam Street, London W1M 5AH.

Editors Preface

Prom Praise has been presented for over 20 years as a musical celebration of the Christian faith. It features a lively orchestral concert and much enthusiastic audience participation - just like the "Last Night of the Proms".

In the 8 years since the release of Prom Praise Solos Volume One, the popularity of 'Prom Praise' events has soared with visits to Ireland, Russia, Scotland, Wales, centres throughout England and similar events in South Africa, USA, Canada, Australia and New Zealand by other groups inspired by the All Souls Orchestra's work. In 1997 the All Souls Orchestra celebrated its 25th Year. What better way to commemorate this occasion than with a new volume of vocal solos, a selection of 10 songs taken from our current and ever increasing repertoire that have brought much blessing and encouragement to both listeners and performers alike.

By providing such a resource, we hope that people will be encouraged to take these songs into their churches, using them in their expression of adoration and worship of God. We would not be able to do this without the co-operation of many people. Our thanks are due to all the composers, arrangers and lyricists who have given permission for their work to be included in this collection. Their God-given talent has inspired us in countless Prom Praises and we are delighted to be the means to pass this on to an even wider audience.

This volume is a joint production between Langham Arts and Christian Focus Publications. I wish to thank in particular London Bible College and their Music & Worship Department, for making it possible for me to prepare this volume for publication as one of my papers and James Couper-Johnston, General Manager of Langham Arts for his encouragement and dedication in seeing this project become a reality - it has certainly been a most challenging and rewarding time.

Timothy Robb
June 1997

As Water To The Thirsty

Words: Timothy Dudley-Smith
Music: Brian Coleman
arranged: Noël Tredinnick

*Small Notes: these are for a solo instrument

Eagles Fly

Words and music: Steve Ragsdale
arranged: Merion Powell

To be spoken at the outset:

> Do you not know? Have you not heard? The Lord is the everlasting God, the Creator of the ends of the earth. He will not grow tired or weary, and his understanding no-one can fathom. He gives strength to the weary and increases the power of the weak. Even youths grow tired and weary, and young men stumble and fall; but those who ***hope in the Lord** will renew their strength. They will soar on wings like eagles; they will run and not grow weary, they will walk and not be faint.

*Begin Music

12

He Became Like A Man
(The Name Of Jesus)

Words & Music: Kevin Jones
arranged: Noël Tredinnick

*Small notes: for these, the voice could be replaced by a solo instrument.

He's Alive!
(A Song For Easter)

Words and Music: Christian Strover

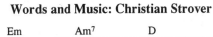

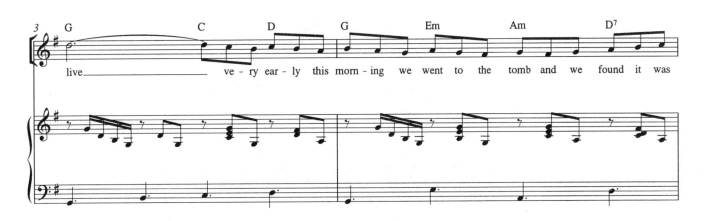

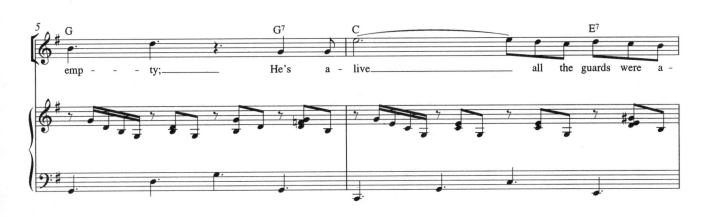

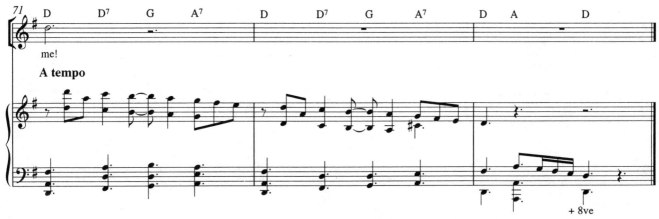

I Wish We'd All Been Ready

Words and Music: Larry Norman
arranged: Noël Tredinnick

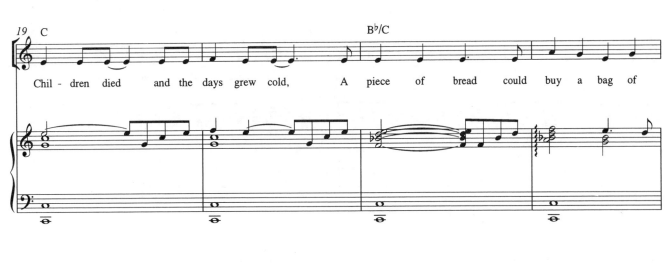

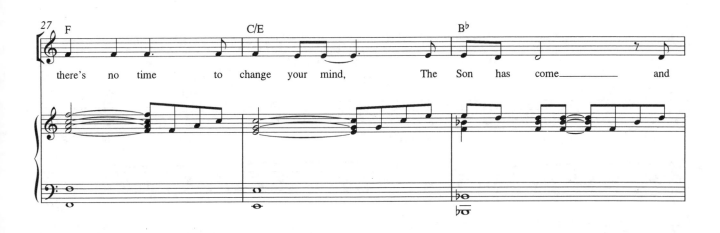

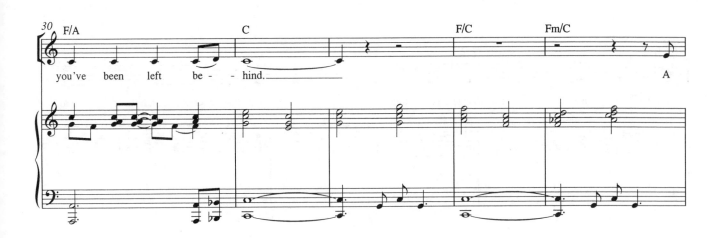

People Need The Lord

Words and Music:
Greg Nelson & Phil McHugh

Thorns In The Straw
(Since The Day The Angel Came)

Words and Music: Graham Kendrick
arranged: Jonathan Rathbone

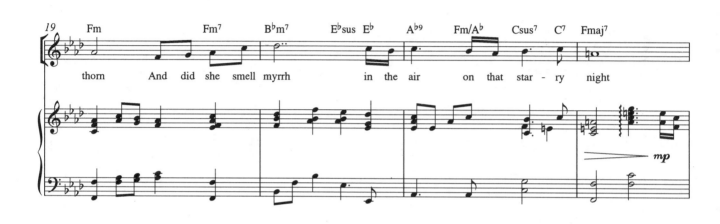

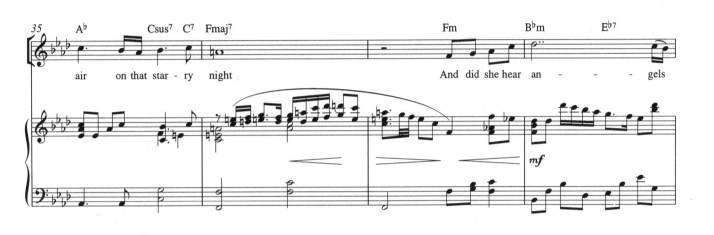

Were You There?

Traditional American Spiritual
arranged: Noël Tredinnick

With Loving Hands

Words: Randle Manwaring
Music: Noël Tredinnick

Words Of Praise

Words and Music: Ken Medema
arranged: Noël Tredinnick

48